Usborne
Sticker Dolly Dressing
Unicorns

Illustrated by Antonia Miller

Written by Fiona Watt

Contents

Rainbows in the sky

When the sun is shining brightly, but raindrops begin to fall, Violet and Rosa paint rainbows across the sky. Unicorns usually appear and soar gracefully around them.

Violet

Rosa

3

Springtime

As the cold sleepy months of winter drift away and the days become warmer, springtime buds burst into flower. Flora and Hester love wandering with their unicorns to watch the bees and butterflies that appear in search of sweet-smelling pollen and nectar.

Celandine

Flora

Hester

Columbine

Stepping stones

Mimosa and Clover tiptoe daintily across stepping stones at the edge of a pond to play with Moonflower and her foal, Rosehip. Clover throws bubbles into the air for Rosehip to burst on the tip of her horn.

Moonflower

Rosehip

Mimosa

Clover

Woodland walk

Princess Cora and Princess Faye live in a magnificent palace with their parents, the king and queen. Every afternoon they collect their unicorns from the royal stables and take them for a walk in the shady woodlands that surround the palace.

Cora

Willow

Catching snowflakes

When snow tumbles silently from the icy sky, Crystal and Avaline fly high above the snowy ground to try to catch as many snowflakes as they can. They're joined by flying unicorns that prance and flutter around them.

Cryst

Avaline

Starry sky

When the sky is illuminated with dancing purple and green lights, Luna and Aurora leap onto their unicorns and ride up into the stars. Shimmering fairy dust flows from their wands as they cast magical wishes for sleeping children everywhere.

Luna

Astra

Aurora

Starlight

Beside the sea

Unicorns and mermaids love to dive into the sea and play together in the gentle waves. Other sea creatures often hear the sound of the mermaids' laughter and come to join in the fun.

Marina

Oriana

Fontana

Meriel

15

In the orchard

Sunbeam and her foal, Twinkle, are dozing in the dappled shade beneath the branches of an old apple tree. Pippin and Dewberry are picking fruit from the tree, but Ambrosia is worried that they might disturb the sleepy unicorns.

Pippin

Sunbeam

Dewberry

Ambrosia

An enchanted forest

In a clearing in a forest, delicate notes flow from Melody's flute and dance between the lantern-lit trees. Unicorns, entranced by the beautiful music, stand silently in the shadows, while glowing fireflies flutter around in the cool night air.

Moonb

Sk

Melody

In the moonlight

Every evening, if the night sky is clear, Queen Marilla leaves her palace and strolls around the royal estate to look at the moon and the twinkling stars. Caspian, her trusty unicorn, always trots silently beside her and leads her safely through the darkness.

Caspian

Leaping waterfalls

Unicorns leap through the cool water that cascades down a magnificent waterfall. When they are tired they climb out of the water to dry their wings, before flying off to play again.

Sweetpea

Stitchwort

Briar

Serena

Making daisy chains

In a sunny clearing at the edge of a forest, Kitty sits making delicate garlands from daisies that she has gathered. She'll make one for herself and some for Larkspur to wear on his head and around his neck.

Larkspur

First published in 2019 by Usborne Publishing Ltd., on Hill, London, EC1N , ngland. www.usbo m
Copyright © 2019 Usborne Publishing Ltd. The name Us e devices 🎈🎠 are Trade Marks of Usborne Pu ing Ltd.
All rights reserved. No part of this publication may be reprodu d in a retrieval system, or transmitted in any form any means, electronic, mechanical, photocopy, recording or otherwise, wit rior permission of the publisher. UE. First published in merica 2019.